OOR WULLIE FUNBOOKS
CRIVVENS!

Why are snakes so hard to fool?

Because they have no legs to pull!

OOR WULLIE

Wull doesna get a minute's peace
From Soapy and Fat Bob.
It's work, work, work, until he goes
And gets himsel' a job!

SCHOOL HOLIDAYS ARE GREAT! I'M GOIN' TAE LIE IN BED THE WHOLE DAY!

OH, NO, YE'RE NOT! I WANT TAE GET THIS ROOM CLEANED!

OOT YE GET! WE'RE NO' ALL ON HOLIDAY!

AW, MA!

BUMP!

I'LL GO BACK TAE BED WHEN SHE'S FINISHED!

NO YE'LL NOT! YE CAN CUT THE GRASS FOR ME!

ACH!

I'LL KEEP MY JAMMIES ON AND GO BACK TAE BED AS SOON AS I'VE CUT THE GRASS!

MICHT AS WELL READ MY BEANO WHILE I'M DAEIN' IT!

EEK! MY FLOWERS!

HEY, WULLIE — AS SOON AS YE'VE FINISHED THAT JOB YE CAN HELP ME!

EH?

I'VE GOT A JOB DELIVERIN' LEAFLETS, BUT IT'S HARD WORK, AND YE OWE ME A FAVOUR SINCE YE CRASHED MY CARTIE THE ITHER DAY!

HUH! MY LONG LIE'S STARTIN' TAE VANISH!

ACH, STOP MOANIN'! AT LEAST YE'RE ON HOLIDAY — I'M WORKIN'!

HERE, HAE A LEAFLET!

There's a black cat in your kitchen.

That's good.
Black cats are lucky.

Not really. This one is eating the fish you were going to have for dinner.

A TRICKY TALE
by
Oor Wullie

Wullie fancies himself as a story-teller — and a rhymer, too!

To read his funny tale, all you have to do is fit in the right word which rhymes with the words or phrase in italics.

Once upon a *nursery rhyme* there lived a wizard named Tricky McTurk. This *icy blizzard* spent his time putting *sea-shells* on people. This he did by *close-shaving* his magic wand over his victim and *stuttering* his magic *dicky-birds.*

Then, one *River Tay*, Tricky popped a *bicycle bell* on wee Eck Soutar. This *Motherwell* made *horse's neck* do everything the opposite way round; if Eck was told to turn to the *awfy fright,* he would *mountain burn* to the left instead; if Eck's *smoky lum* gave him her muddy *bus queues* to clean, he would put more *roasted spud* on them.

But this was Tricky's undoing. He was *silk stocking* through a wood when a gale sprang up. This gale knocked over a tall *queen bee* which fell on Tricky.

Wee Eck was passing and saw the *scaly lizard's* plight.
"Get this *North Sea* off me!" bawled Tricky.
But *quarter-deck* was still under the *nasty smell.* Instead of lifting the *door-key* off Tricky he piled on another dozen *knobbly knees.*
Tricky never removed a *prison cell* faster than he did that time.

OOR WULLIE'S FUN SECTION

"Aye, that's a fine dog you've got. Is he faithful?"

"He is that! I've sold him five times and he's always come back!"

Two young doctors met for the first time since they were at college together. "I'm specialising in nerve treatment," said one.

"And have you had any success?" asked the other.

"I should say so!" was the reply. "Why, when I had finished with my last case, the patient had enough nerve to ask for the loan of ten pounds!"

* * *

Absent-minded Man (who has just been rescued from drowning) — "Dash it, I've just remembered that I can swim!"

"I don't think anyone will ever give us work!"

"Oh, I could work for anyone I please!"

"Why don't you, then?"

"I don't seem to please anyone!"

Old Sailor — "Did I find it hot out in the Tropics? I should say it was hot! Why, one day I went ashore, and a crowd of cannibals started chasing me, and, believe me, it was so hot that we all walked!"

* * *

Father — "How are you getting on at the office?"

Son — "Fine! The boss says I've got everything so mixed up that he can't do without me."

"Somebody left this bottle of milk on my bus."

"Take it to the 'Lost Property'. If it's not claimed in six months, it's yours."

A friend asked Tom why he was poking a pound note through a hole in the pavement.

"If you must know," retorted Tom, "I've dropped a five penny piece down there, and I want to make it worth while to tear up the pavement so's I can get it back!"

* * *

"Hullo, bought a saxaphone?"

"No, I borrowed it from the man next door."

"But you can't play it."

"Neither can he while I've got it!"

"What's up, Davie? Been fightin' again?"

"Na. We've been flittin', and I had tae carry Ma's cactus plants!"

Doctor — "Do your teeth chatter when you're in bed?"

Patient — "I don't know. I always leave them in the bathroom."

* * *

MacDougal — "You are a chauffeur? Can you give me a reference from your last employer?"

MacFarlane — "Not for a month or so."

MacDougal — "Why not?"

MacFarlane — "He's still in hospital."

"What's wrong, man Homesick?"

"No, sir—heresick!"

WULLIE'S TOP TEN!

HIDDEN IN THESE SQUARES ARE TEN OF WULLIE'S FAVOURITE THINGS AND PEOPLE. THE WORDS, WHICH ARE LISTED BELOW, ARE WRITTEN ACROSS, UP, DOWN, DIAGONALLY— AND EVEN BACKWARDS! SEE HOW QUICKLY YOU CAN SPOT THEM!

GOBSTOPPER: CONKERS: SWEETS: BRIDIES: P.C.MURDOCH: MARBLES: FAT BOB: BICYCLE: SOAPY: ECK..

R	E	P	P	O	T	S	B	O	G
F	B	Y	W	T	J	O	I	H	C
H	R	E	R	M	B	H	C	K	O
S	I	E	X	T	Y	O	Y	Y	N
T	D	R	A	J	D	P	C	P	K
E	I	F	L	R	M	L	L	A	E
E	E	D	U	W	K	C	E	O	R
W	S	M	A	R	B	L	E	S	S
S	C	J	R	F	N	P	U	T	K
P	O	L	I	M	A	T	K	W	J

HELP M'BOAB

SEE HOW MANY WORDS YOU CAN MAKE, USING THE LETTERS IN **HELP M'BOAB**. PLURALS AND PROPER NAMES ARE NOT ALLOWED. PUT YOUR WORDS IN THE SPACE BELOW.

20 WORDS – SO-SO.
25 WORDS – BETTER.
30 WORDS – BRAW.
OVER 30 WORDS – JINGS!

OOR WULLIE

When Wullie's doubled up wi' pain,
The doc's place sure is handy.
Alas, oor wee chum soon finds out
This ploy is far from "dandy"!

I'M WRESTLIN' WI' A REAL TRICKY PROBLEM TODAY!

I THINK I'VE GOT THE ANSWER!

SURGERY
DR. DIRE

OOH! OW! THE PAIN ... IT'S AFFY!

IT'S APPENDATHINGUMMY, OR AN IN-GROWIN' TOE-NAIL MEBBE. THANK GUIDNESS I'M RICHT BESIDE THE DOCTOR'S!

OOH! AAGH! HELP! GASP!

GOODNESS!

RECEPTION

LUCKY I'M HERE WI' MY AMBULANCE. I'LL GET THE STRETCHER!

WE'LL GET HIM TAE THE HOSPITAL RIGHT AWAY!

IT'S A'RICHT, MISTER, I'M NO' THAT BAD. IN FACT, I'M FULLY RECOVERED!

EH?

THAT DIDNA WORK! I'LL HAE TAE THINK O' SOMETHIN' ELSE.

STRANGE BOY!

THE VERY DAB!

DENTIST

OOH! AAH! OW!

WHAT IS IT? WHAT'S WRONG?

AW ... AW ... AW ... !

TAKE A SEAT! THE DENTIST WILL SEE YOU AFTER HE'S ATTENDED TO MRS GREEN HERE.

Can I have a nice fluffy toy for my little girl?

Sorry, Madam, we don't do exchanges!

PLAY the GAME!

PLAY THE GAME DIRECTIONS. LAY THE SKETCH DOWN ON A FLAT SURFACE, THEN TAKE TURNS, WITH TWO OR MORE PLAYERS, DROPPING A SMALL COIN ON THE CIRCLES FROM ABOUT A FOOT ABOVE THE GAME. ADD ALL THE NUMBERS THAT ARE IN THE SECTIONS TOUCHED BY THE COIN. THE PLAYER WITH THE LARGEST SCORE AFTER FIVE TRIES IS THE WINNER.

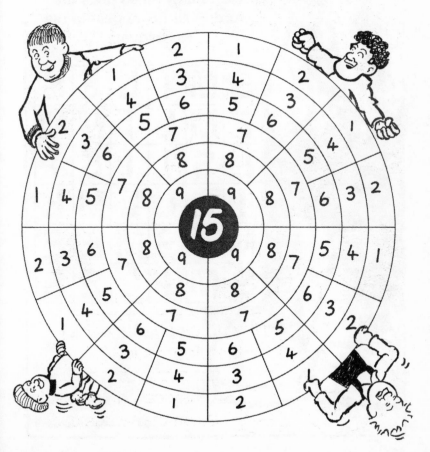

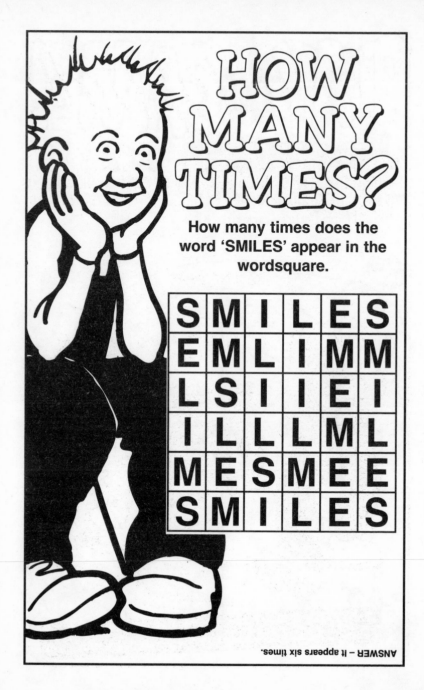

HOW MANY TIMES?

How many times does the word 'SMILES' appear in the wordsquare.

S	M	I	L	E	S
E	M	L	I	M	M
L	S	I	I	E	I
I	L	L	L	M	L
M	E	S	M	E	E
S	M	I	L	E	S

Just Joking!

Customer: "Waiter, there's a fly in my alphabet soup!"
Waiter: "It must be learning to read, sir!"

What do you get when you cross an insect and a rabbit?

Bugs Bunny!

What would you do if you were in my shoes?

Clean them!

What did one strawberry say to another strawberry?

How did we get into this jam!

What's big and hairy and flies at two hundred miles per hour?

King Kong-cord!

TRAMP: "Can I cut your grass for my dinner!"
LADY: "Of course you can, and I hope you enjoy eating it!"

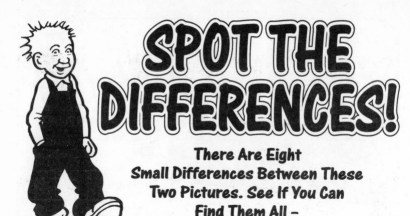

SPOT THE DIFFERENCES!

**There Are Eight
Small Differences Between These
Two Pictures. See If You Can
Find Them All –**

OOR WULLIE

Wull has a way wi' big fierce dogs —
He puts them in their place.
But jings, he shudders when he sees
This big brute's angry face!

I THINK I'LL AWA' AN' SEE FAT BOB.

AND SO ....

HULLO, BOB.

HI, WULLIE! DAE ME A FAVOUR ...

... DELIVER THAT PAPER TAE No. 23 THE BAD-TEMPERED BRUTE IN THERE TERRIFIES ME!

SCARED O' A DUG, ARE YE? HUH!

B-BUT ..!

BUTCH DISNAE SCARE ME!

AYE, BUT ...

STOP!

SEE WHIT I MEAN?

AYE, BUT ...

THERE, GOOD DOG!

OH, JUMP UP AT ME, WID YE!

I'LL HAE TAE TEACH YOU MANNERS! LIE!

Why was the Egyptian child worried?

Because her daddy was a mummy!

Waiter, this egg is bad!

Don't blame me, sir, I only lay the tables!

NOW, WILLIAM, WHERE ARE THE ANDES?

ON THE END O' YER WRISTIES, SIR!

Are you brighter than Wullie? See how you score in this quiz!

1. **How many legs has an an insect?**
2. Who completed the first aeroplane crossing of the English Channel?
3. **What is portrayed on the reverse side of a penny coin?**
4. Fir Park is the home of which Scottish football club?
5. **In a sailing boat, what are the halyards?**
6. Who wrote "The Swallows and the Amazons"?
7. **What is the meaning of the road sign which shows a bicycle inside a red circle?**
8. A funny one — why is tennis such a noisy game?
9. **"Wisden" is an annual book about which sport?**
10. Who was the first man in space?

11. **In which two sports are mallets used?**
12. What is the capital of Canada?
13. **At which battle was Lord Nelson killed?**
14. When does a ship fly the Blue Peter flag?
15. **In which building complex is the U.S.A. gold bullion stored?**
16. Who "picked a peck of pickled pepper"?
17. **Which alphabet consists of a series of dots?**
18. Who wrote the fable about the hare and the tortoise?

19. **Who led an army of elephants over the Alps?**
20. Which travels faster — light or sound?
21. **A farmer had seventeen cows. All but five died. How many did he have left?**
22. In what pantomime story is Never-Never Land?
23. **If a clock in a mirror says it is 3.35, what time is it?**
24. "Face-off" is a term in which sport?
25. **By what other name is Pancake Day known?**

ANSWERS — 1, Six. 2, Louis Blériot. 3, A portcullis. 4, Motherwell F.C. 5, The ropes used to pull up the sails. 6, Arthur Ransome. 7, No cycling or moped-riding. 8, Because both players raise a racket 9, Cricket. 10, Yuri Gagarin. 11, Polo and croquet. 12, Ottawa. 13, Trafalgar, 1805. 14, When it is about to sail. 15, Fort Knox. 16, Peter Piper. 17, The Braille Alphabet. 18, Aesop. 19, Hannibal. 20, Light. 21, Five! 22, "Peter Pan". 23, 8.25. 24, Ice hockey. 25, Shrove Tuesday.

Try to find at least FIFTEEN objects in this picture which begin with the letter "R".

Teaser Time

BLUEBIRD·OSTRICH·PARROT·ORIOLE·CARDINAL
CONDOR·DUCK·PHEASANT·DODO·EAGLE·HEN
KITE·EMU·LARK·AUK·WREN·JAY·SPARROW·OWL

CAN YOU PRINT THE NAMES OF THE ABOVE 19 BIRDS IN THE EMPTY SQUARES, SO THEY WILL READ ACROSS, AND DOWN, AS IN A CROSSWORD PUZZLE? WE'VE GIVEN YOU A START!

2·7·12·17
22·27·32
37·42

WRITE THE ABOVE NUMBERS IN THE CIRCLES TO MAKE EACH OF THE FOUR STRAIGHT LINES OF FIGURES ADD TO EXACTLY **66**

ANSWERS

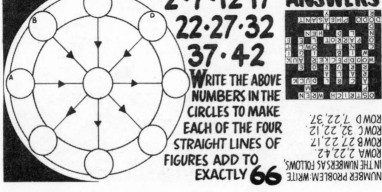

NUMBER PROBLEM: WRITE IN THE NUMBERS AS FOLLOWS,
ROW A 2, 22, 42.
ROW B 27, 22, 17.
ROW C 32, 22, 12.
ROW D 7, 22, 37.

A FEAST OF FUN!

START FROM CERTAIN LETTERED PLATES AND MOVE ALONG THE LINES TO THE NEXT PLATE, AND SO ON, TO SEE IF YOU CAN SPELL THE NAMES OF EIGHT DIFFERENT FOODS...

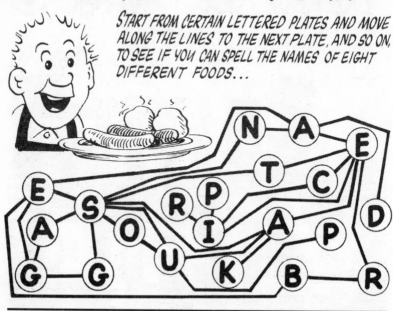

HIDDEN IN EACH OF THE FOLLOWING FIVE SENTENCES IS A FRUIT. SEE HOW QUICKLY YOU CAN FIND ALL FIVE...

1. HAND ME OVER THAT MAP PLEASE, IRENE.

2. MUM SAYS TO SHOP EARLY AND AVOID THE CROWDS.

3. ON HIS CAP EACH BOY WORE A BADGE.

4. WHAT LITTLE MONEY I HAVE, I'M WILLING TO SHARE.

5. I THINK THE MAID ATE THE LAST CAKE, SAID COOK.

Move It!

Hidden in the square is a nine-letter word associated with Oor Wullie – once you have found it, how many other words of three or more letters can you find, by moving from one square to the next in any direction? You may not go through the same square twice in any one word.

E	R	D
E	A	U
S	G	N

18 – 20 words (Good)
20 – 25 words (Excellent)
Over 25 words (Genius!)

CARTOON TIME

OOR WULLIE

Oor Wullie's up to ninety-nine!
He eats so much that he's
As fat as Bob — and what is worse.
Too big for his dungarees!

CAN I HAE ANITHER EGG, MAW?

I SUPPOSE SO! SIGH!

YE MICHT AS WELL PIT ANITHER TWA BITS O' BREAD INTAE THE PAN WI' THE EGGS!

BACON AS WELL! BRAW!

YE'RE GOIN' TAE END UP LIKE BOB — FAT WULLIE!

AWA'!

OUTSIDE —

OH, HO! THERE'S P.C. MURDOCH! HE DISNA LOOK VERY PLEASED WI' ME!

I'LL NIP THROUGH THE HOLE IN TAM WILSON'S FENCE!

MEANWHILE —

THAT'S ONE NEW PLANK IN, I'LL GO AN' GET THE ITHER ANE!

HO-HO! MURDOCH'S TOO FAT TAE GET THROUGH HERE!

CRIVVENS! I'M TOO FAT AS WELL!

I'LL HIDE UP GROUSER GREEN'S TREE! MURDOCH WINNA FIND ME THERE!

AT THAT MOMENT —

IT'S TIME THIS AULD BRANCH WIS CUT BACK!

COOEE, TAM, I'VE POURED YE A CUP O' TEA!

JIST COMIN'!

Doctor, a dog has just bitten my leg!

Did you put anything on it?

No, he seemed to like it just the way it was!

Why did the robber take a bath?

So he could make a clean get away!

Fun In The Sun!

Wullie has taken his bucket to the beach. Unscramble the words below to discover six other items he took with him.

DAPES Spades
LABL Ball
SALKF Flask
DOOF Food
TSUNKR Trunks
GELSOGG Goggles

HORSE	· HOWL
HYENA	· BRAY
SNAKE	· COO
WOLF	· HISS
ASS	· CHATTER
FROG	· LAUGH
DOVE	· NEIGH
MONKEY	· CROAK

ANIMAL ANTICS

EEL	· CALF
SWAN	· LEVERET
FOX	· KID
HARE	· CYGNET
ELEPHANT	· PUP
SEAL	· FOAL
HORSE	· CUB
GOAT	· ELVER

· A N S W E R S ·

ANIMALS CRY:— HORSE, NEIGH; HYENA, LAUGH; SNAKE, HISS; WOLF, HOWL; ASS, BRAY; FROG, CROAK; DOVE, COO; MONKEY, CHATTER.

YOUNG ONES:— EEL, ELVER; SWAN, CYGNET; FOX, CUB; HARE, LEVERET; ELEPHANT, CALF; SEAL, PUP; HORSE, FOAL; GOAT, KID.

OOR WULLIE

A comb fit for a baldie,
A brolly for the Fair Isle.
The things in Wullie's car boot sale
Are sure tae mak' ye smile!

HMPH! SKINT AGAIN!

COOEE, WULLIE! ME AN' YER PA ARE AWA' TAE THE BOOLIN' CLUB CAR BOOT SALE!

WISSAT? CAR BOOT SALE?

I CAN SELL THIS... AND THIS... AND THIS AS WELL!

HI, LADS! YE'RE JIST IN TIME! I'VE GOT BARGAINS GALORE HERE!

WULLIE'S GREAT CAR BOOT SALE

TAK' YER PICK!

WHIT'S THIS?

THAT? OH, ER, IT'S A COMB FOR A BALD MANNIE. IT WID DAE YER FAITHER FINE, SAMMY!

YE'RE TOO LATE, WULLIE! MY PA BOUGHT A WIG LAST WEEK!

HUH!

THIS ISNAE MUCH GUID — IT'S GOT A BIG HOLE IN IT!

NA, NA! THAT'S SO YE CAN DAE THE WATERING TWICE AS FAST. WATCH!

Did you hear about the frog who became a secret agent?

He wanted to be a croak and dagger man!

I say, waiter, why is my food all mashed up?

Well, you did ask me to step on it, sir!

Hide and Seek

Hidden in these squares are eleven of Oor Wullie's favourite characters from fiction. The names are written across, up, down, diagonally and even backwards! See how quickly you can find them all!

Here are the names:— **Indiana Jones, Robin Hood, Batman, Lassie, Tarzan, Superman, Heidi, Ivanhoe, Rocky, Tonto, Spiderman.**

O	S	P	I	D	E	R	M	A	N	T	P
W	X	R	N	A	M	E	P	Y	S	W	K
L	K	O	O	L	X	L	G	I	U	U	L
E	L	B	A	T	M	A	N	D	P	T	M
O	P	I	S	K	Y	S	F	I	E	S	J
H	T	N	P	W	K	S	J	E	R	R	B
N	R	H	A	M	C	I	N	H	M	P	O
A	R	O	X	Z	O	E	T	B	A	T	K
V	J	O	K	S	R	M	L	P	N	W	T
I	N	D	I	A	N	A	J	O	N	E	S
N	M	W	O	T	N	O	T	Y	D	H	L

Answers:▼

GOING DOTTY

CONNECT ALL THE DOTS IN ALPHABETICAL ORDER

THE ANSWERS TO THESE SUMS WILL BE NUMBERS FROM ONE TO TWENTY.

WHEN YOU HAVE COMPLETED THEM, CONNECT ALL THE DOTS IN THEIR ORDER TO DRAW A COMPLETE PICTURE.

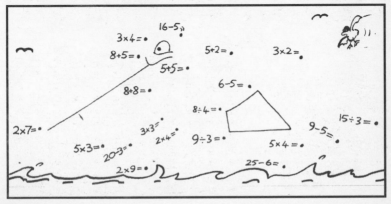

$3 \times 4 =$

$8 + 5 =$

$16 - 5 =$

$5 + 5 =$

$5 + 2 =$

$3 \times 2 =$

$8 + 8 =$

$6 - 5 =$

$8 \div 4 =$

$2 \times 7 =$

$3 \times 3 =$

$2 \times 4 =$

$9 \div 3 =$

$9 - 5 =$

$15 \div 3 =$

$5 \times 3 =$

$20 - 3 =$

$5 \times 4 =$

$2 \times 9 =$

$25 - 6 =$

All Mixed Up!

These Scottish place names have become all jumbled up. Can you identify them?

KIWC

NABO

HEPTR

OONDUN

EPALISY

ANSWERS
Clockwise from the top:–
WICK, PERTH, PAISLEY,
DUNOON, OBAN

SPOT the DIFFERENCE

There are EIGHT small differences between these two pictures. See if you can find them all –

ANSWERS

Knob on clock; Fruit in dish; Teapot; Flower on vase; Door handle; Spot on dog's back; Bob's sock; Drawer handle.

QUIZ BIZ!

WHAT WOULD YOU HAVE IF YOU HAD THREE POUNDS IN ONE POCKET AND FIVE POUNDS IN THE OTHER?

SOMEBODY ELSE'S TROOSERS, MISS!

Are you brighter than Wullie? See how you score in this quiz!

1. In what adventure story is there a parrot called Captain Flint?

2. In which sport is a puck used?

3. Which famous voyager sailed in the "Santa Maria"?

4. What does a barograph measure?

5. How many sides does a 20p coin have?

6. In rhyming slang, what is meant by "plates of meat"?

7. What is a cricket umpire signalling if he raises both arms above his head?

8. What range of hills lies between Scotland and England?

9. Baghdad is the capital city of which country?

10. What was the name of Captain Bligh's ship?

11. How many players are in an American football side?

12. Who was particularly fond of marmalade sandwiches?

13. Is Wednesday the third or the fourth day of the week?

14. What does the abbreviation U.F.O. represent?

15. Nelson's column stands in which London square?

16. Guinea pigs don't have tails — true or false?

17. If it takes five men five days to paint five houses, how long will it take ten men to paint ten houses, working at the same rate?

18. Which football team is known as the Gunners?

19. Which two fruits use the same letters to spell their names?

20. William Tell is a legendary hero of which country?

21. What's strange about locking a piano?

22. Which is heavier — an ounce of copper or an ounce of lead?

23. Which insect has the same name as a sport?

ANSWERS

1. "Treasure Island".
2. Ice hockey.
3. Christopher Columbus.
4. Atmospheric pressure.
5. Seven. 6. Feet.
7. A boundary six.
8. The Cheviot Hills.
9. Iraq. 10. H.M.S. Bounty.
11. Eleven. 12. Paddington Bear. 13. Fourth.
14. Unidentified Flying Object.
15. Trafalgar Square. 16. True.
17. Five days. 18. Arsenal F.C.
19. Lemon and melon.
20. Switzerland. 21. The keys are locked inside!
22. They both weigh an ounce!
23. Cricket.

Doctor, doctor, I feel like the moon!

I can't see you now, come back tonight!

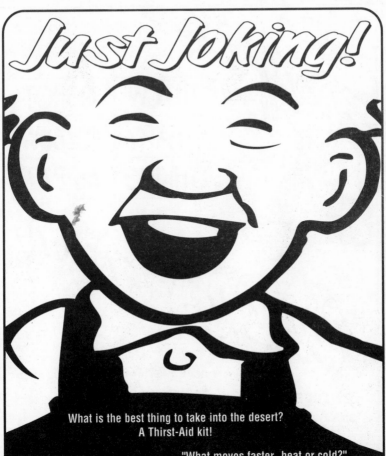

Just Joking!

What is the best thing to take into the desert?
A Thirst-Aid kit!

Knock! Knock!
Who's there?
Arthur
Arthur who?
Arthur any biscuits left?

"What moves faster, heat or cold?"
"I haven't got a clue!"
"Heat of course – you can catch a cold!"

What is green and jumps out of the soup pot?
Spring Cabbage!

TEACHER – "You'd be a good dancer if it weren't for two things."
PUPIL – "What are they?"
TEACHER – "Your feet!"

Two flies were on a cereal packet. "Why are we running so fast?" asked one.
"Because," said the second, "It says 'Tear along dotted line'!"

CAN YOU JUGGLE EACH GROUP OF LETTERS TO SPELL THE NAMES OF SIX FANCY-DRESS COSTUMES?

1. HITCW	2. GSHOT
3. IFARY	4. COYBOW
5. THKING	6. RIPEAT

ALL DRESSED UP!

NOW UNSCRAMBLE THE LETTERS BELOW TO FIND OUT WHAT THE BOLD SIR WILLIAM MIGHT NEED FOR HIS COSTUME.

1. WORDS	2. SIDLEH
3. HEMLET	4. SHORE
5. NECAL	6. OURRAM

Try to find at least twenty items in this picture which start with the letter "W"

OOR WULLIE

A game of cricket? No such luck!
His pals don't want to play.
But trust Oor Wullie! He still has
A "smashing" time today!

IT'S A BRAW DAY FOR A GEMME O' CRICKET!

I'VE GOT A' THE GEAR! NOW TAE FIND THE LADS!

HOW ABOOT A GEMME O' CRICKET, ECK?

CRICKET .... WI' YOU? YOU MUST BE JOKIN'!

THE LAST TIME WE PLAYED, YOU SMASHED OOR BACK WINDIE!

AND ....

CRICKET? NAE CHANCE! I'M STILL PAYIN' FOR THE GLASS YE BROKE IN MY PA'S GREENHOOSE!

THEN ....

CRICKET? YOU MUST BE JOKIN'! YE SMASHED MY FAITHER'S SHED WINDIE LAST TIME!

HMPH! A' THIS GEAR, AND NAE CHUMS TAE PLAY WI'!

THEN ....

SOMEBODY'S NO' HAPPY!

SOB!

THE WIND BLEW DOWN MY NICE SUNFLOWER!

AW!

THERE YE ARE, MAISIE! TIED TAE MY CRICKET STUMP, IT'S AS GUID AS NEW!

ACH, WELL, I'M NO' BREAKIN' ANY WINDIES!

RAT-A-TAT!

LESS O' THE NOISE! YE'LL GET THESE BACK WHEN I'VE HAD MY SNOOZE!

CHEEK!

HERE, SANDY, TAK' THESE! AND KEEP OOT O' HIS REACH THIS TIME!

What happened to the man who crossed an electric blanket with a toaster?

He kept popping out of bed all night!

OOR WULLIE'S FUN SECTION

"What made you decide to buy a dachshund, sir?"

"All the family will be able to pat it at the same time!"

Henry — "How did your Ma know you didn't take a bath?"

Hamish — "I forgot to wet the soap."

• • •

Diner — "A glass of water, please."

Waiter — "For drinking?"

Diner (sarcastically) — "No. I want to wash my feet."

• • •

Visitor — "What are you going to be when you grow up, Jimmy?"

Jimmy — "Well, after I've been a doctor to please Ma and a judge to please Pa, I'm going to be a sailor to please myself."

"I'll never forget where I first drew this sword!"

"Where?"

"In a raffle!"

Ian — "Do you know who wears the biggest hat in town?"

Jim — "No — who?"

Ian — "The man with the biggest head."

• • •

McTosh — "Did you tell McAllister that I had the biggest feet you have ever seen?"

McDougall — "No. I just said that if you took your boots off you would be half undressed."

"Will you sit on my right hand?"

"Won't you need it for holding your knife?"

"Boy!" said the guest in a small hotel. "Dash up to room sixty-five and see if my raincoat is hanging behind the door. Hurry, because I have a train to catch!"

In a few minutes, the boy returned.

"Yes, sir," he said. "It's there, just as you said."

• • •

Teacher — "Putting a drawing-pin on a teacher's chair is a stupid old joke."

Tommy — "Yes, sir, but it hasn't lost its point."

• • •

"Get out of my way, you little squirt!"

McTavish — "I see McKay has bought another new car.

McAllister — "Aye, he says he went into a garage to use the phone and didn't like to come out without buying something."

• • •

"See that waiter over there? They call him 'Tomorrow'."

"Why is that?"

"Because he never comes!"

• • •

Bore — "Yes, football is a dangerous game. Last year I was knocked senseless while playing!"

Listener — "When do you expect to recover?"

"Here, Lizzie Smith, I've been told you've been calling me a bookworm!"

"Who said anything about books?"

A FEAST OF FUN!

Wullie's treating himself to a knickerbocker glory,
and jumbled up on the menu board are a few of the other
things your wee chum also loves to eat or drink.
Can you unscramble them all?

BARGE SHRUM   BANS PILANAT
SNAP BAND EEI   IS VOTES
CHAP FINS DISH   MAKE SILK H

SEE HOW MANY WORDS YOU CAN MAKE USING THE LETTERS IN 'NAE FISHING'! PLURALS AND PROPER NOUNS ARE NOT ALLOWED. PUT YOUR WORDS IN THE SPACE BELOW.

HOW DID YOU SCORE? 15 WORDS OR LESS — TRY AGAIN! 15-20. NOT SO BAD! 20-25. BRAINBOX! OVER 25 - CRIVVENS!

Who Goes Where?

Can you pair the following characters with the television show, film or book in which they appear?

1. THE DURSLEYS	SABRINA THE TEENAGE WITCH
2. BARNEY RUBBLE	A CHRISTMAS CAROL
3. HAROLD BISHOP	RUGRATS
4. THE ARTFUL DODGER	THE MUPPETS
5. LITTLE MO	THE FLINTSTONES
6. CHANDLER	NEIGHBOURS
7. ANGELICA	HARRY POTTER
8. SABRINA	OLIVER TWIST
9. EBENEEZER SCROOGE	FRIENDS
10. MISS PIGGY	EASTENDERS

ANSWERS

1. The Dursleys – Harry Potter. 2. Barney Rubble – The Flintstones.
3. Harold Bishop – Neighbours. 4. The Artful Dodger – Oliver Twist.
5. Little Mo – Eastenders. 6. Chandler – Friends. 7. Angelica – Rugrats.
8. Sabrina – Sabrina The Teenage Witch.
9. Ebeneezer Scrooge – A Christmas Carol. 10. Miss Piggy – The Muppets.

OOR WULLIE

Pink ice cream and candy floss,
And chips, hauf cauld and greasy.
It seems the perfect recipe
Tae mak' oor lad feel queasy!

DINNA INTERRUPT ME JUST NOO. I'M TRYING TAE WORK OOT A PLAN!

THE PARK FIRST!

A CONE, PLEASE .... WI' PINK ICE CREAM!

HEY, DINNA YOU GET ANY ICE CREAM ON MY TRAMPOLINE!

PLOP!

JINGS! YE DISTRACTED ME THERE. IT'S NO' EASY TAE EAT AND BOUNCE AT THE SAME TIME!

I DIDNAE GET A' THE GOOD O' THAT, BUT IT WAS A START.

AN' THIS ISNAE BAD IF YE SHUT YER EYES!

YOU AGAIN!

CRIVVENS, IT'S NO' EASY TAE KEEP YER BALANCE WHEN YE DINNA LOOK.

CHIPS by Pete

I'VE JUST GOT TIME TAE NIP INTAE GREASY PETE'S . . .

. . . AND STILL CATCH THE BOAT.

PRETTY BAD DAY FOR A TRIP ROON' THE LIGHTHOUSE, WULLIE.

WI' A BIT O' LUCK, IT MIGHT GET WORSE!

PLEASURE CRUISES

Why did Slim Tim eat a brick?

Because he wanted to build himself up!

THANKS, MR WILSON.

HEY! A FUNFAIR — AND A BIG DIPPER!

BUT FIRST, A CANDYFLOSS!

OH, I THINK I'VE REACHED THE LIMIT.

BUT JUST TAE MAKE SURE —

DON'T KNOW WHY YE WANT TO BORROW IT, WULLIE, 'COS IT'S WRECKED. I WAS TAKING IT TO THE DUMP!

JUST WHAT I NEED!

UGH! OOH, THIS IS JUST THE TICKET!

GREEN

ESPECIALLY GOING DOON BARRIE'S BRAE!

HE LOOKS AWFUL!

BACK HOME —

OOH, I FEEL SO ILL, I CANNAE POSSIBLY COME TAE AUNTIE JESSIE'S WI' YE THE DAY!

AYE, HE MUST BE SICKENIN' FOR SOMETHING. HE LOOKS RIGHT HINGY!

BELIEVE ME, A DAY IN BED FEELING SICK IS BETTER THAN HAVING AUNTIE JESSIE SLOBBERIN' A' OWER YE!

LATER —

I'M FEELIN' FINE NOW!

Every time the doorbell rings my dog goes in a corner!

Why is that?

Because he's a boxer!

The NAME GAME

Each picture represents a boys' or girls' first name. Can you guess all ten?

Take Your Pick!

Only two of these nine pictures are the same.
Can you spot which ones?

CARTOON TIME

Shall I tell you a story about a brick wall? No, perhaps not – you might never get over it!

Why did the liquorice sweet go swimming and play football and tennis?

Because it was a liquorice all-sport!

BY PRINTING THE NINE CORRECT NINE-LETTER WORDS IN THE SQUARES READING ACROSS, THE DIAGONAL ROW OF LETTERS READING DOWNWARDS WILL SPELL SOMETHING WHICH OOR WULLIE LIKES!

1. LARGE DOGS.
2. COMING AFTER.
3. WULLIE'S PAL, MURDOCH.

4. LIABLE TO BLOW UP.
5. PARTICULARLY.
6. VANISH.

7. MEAT EATER.
8. INSTRUMENT FOR STAR GAZING.
9. STUPID.

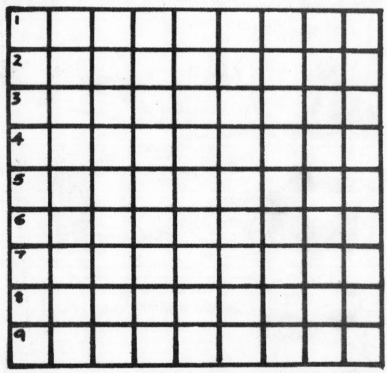

ANSWERS:- 1. LABRADORS. 2. FOLLOWING 3. POLICEMAN 4. EXPLOSIVE. 5. SPECIALLY, 6. DISAPPEAR. 7. CARNIVORE. 8. TELESCOPE. 9. SENSELESS. DIAGONALLY-LOLLIPOPS.

Just Joking!

What's black and white all over and very difficult?
An exam paper!

Did you hear about the man who
went to a fancy dress ball dressed as a biscuit?

A dog ate him up when he got out of his car!

MY BUCKET

What pie can fly?
A Magpie!

What goes up the river at 150 miles per hour?

A motor pike!

LADY: "This loaf is lovely and warm!
BAKER: "So it should be, madam. The cat has been
sitting on it all morning!"

3 × 3 = 7 6

What do you get if you mix a Bear with a Skunk?

Winnie The Pooh!

Animal Crackers

Hidden in these squares are 21 creatures. The names are written across, up, down, diagonally and even backwards! See how quickly you can find them.

```
K A Y R E G I T P C
A M A L L Y N X I H
L V O E E J F T G E
L M M T P W K A P E
I U W F H N F O X T
R P U M A O L T M A
O N K L N E R S B H
G T O R T O I S E A
X Y J N R P F T E J
W P A N T H E R P K
```

To help you, here are the names:-
bee, cheetah, tiger, yak, gorilla, gnu, elephant, puma, antelope, horse, stoat, panther, lemur, lynx, pig, fox, tortoise, llama, moth, mole, ant.

Answers

```
K R E H T N A P W
E T F P R N J Y X
E S I O T R O T G
M B S R E N L K N O
M T L O A M U P R
X O F N H F W U I
E P A K W P T M M L
G T F J E E O V L
H I X N Y L L A M A
C P T I G E R Y A K
```

Why did the man wear two pairs of glasses?

Someone told him that he had second sight!

Can I have a sink, please?

Certainly, sir. Do you want a plug with it?

Gosh, I didn't realise they were electric!

EYE-TWISTERS

DO YOU BELIEVE WHAT YOU SEE?

Is line A B longer or shorter than C D? Is E F longer or shorter than G H? Make your guess —— then measure them to be convinced.

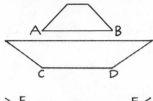

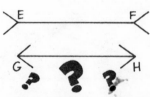

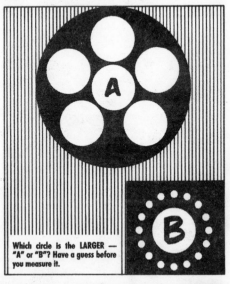

Which circle is the LARGER —— "A" or "B"? Have a guess before you measure it.

WHICH MAN IS TALLER?

Ask your pal to guess – then get a ruler to prove him wrong.

Spot the Differences

**There are eight small differences between
these two pictures. See if you can find them all –**

FIGURE IT OUT!

GET your pal to think of a number, then multiply it by 3, add 6 to the total, and divide it by 3. Ask him for the answer, subtract 2 from it and you have the number he first thought of.

WHILE he's still trying to understand how you worked out that first piece of magic ask him to think of another number, tell him to write it down, then to double it, add 1, multiply by 5, add 5 and multiply by 10. Ask him for his total, subtract 100 from it and strike off the last two figures — then you have the number he first thought of!

> EXAMPLE
> 15×2 = 30
> 30+1 = 31
> 31×5 = 155
> 155+5 = 160
> 160×10 = 1,600
> 1,600-100 = 1,500

NOW get him to try to mark in 4 minus signs between the numbers below, so as to arrive at the answer of 2.

You can have a go at this one too!

7676767676 = 2

This dug brings Wull bad luck galore.
Aye, not one thing goes right.
But life gets better for oor lad –
Thanks to its appetite!

WE'RE LOOKIN' EFTER MRS WILSON'S DUG WHILE SHE'S AWA' TAE HER SISTER'S. HERE, TAK' IT A WALK.

THERE'S GRANPAW BROON! HE AYE HAS PEPPERIES ON PENSION DAY!

HELLO, WULLIE. THAT'S A BRAW DUG YE'VE GOT THERE! AND HE BEGS AS WELL!

AYE!

CLEVER DUG! HERE, HAE MY LAST PEPPERY!

HMPH! FINE PAL YOU ARE!

SOOK

LET'S SEE IF YE CAN BRING BACK STICKS. HERE — FETCH!

CRIVVENS!

OUCH!

TIME TAE HIDE, WILLIAM!

BUT....

OH, NO! GO ON, YE DAFT DUG! BEAT IT!

Angus hasn't had a haircut for ten years.

He must be daft!

He isn't. He's bald.

What is the simplest way to increase your bank balance?

Look at it through a magnifying glass!

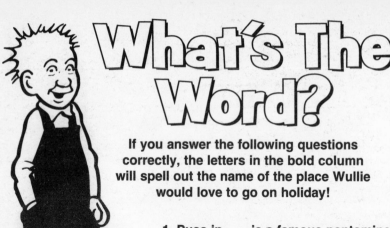

What's The Word?

If you answer the following questions correctly, the letters in the bold column will spell out the name of the place Wullie would love to go on holiday!

1. Puss in ...... is a famous pantomine.
2. Batman's partner.
3. Opposite of hot.
4. This city has a leaning tower.
5. It gives the Earth heat and light.
6. This is Scotland's capital city.
7. Wullie's pet, Jeemy, is one.

1	B	O	O	T	S	
2		R	O	B	I	N
3	C	O	L	D		
4	P	i	s	a		
5	S	u	n			
6	E	D	i	n	B	u	r	g	h
7	M	O	U	S	e	

ANSWERS

TWO FOR YOU!

BBWNSNEFTHSEBKS

Try to print a certain single letter seven times,
in the above letters, so that the combined letters will
form a six-word sentence.

Easy, is it? Right!
Here's the second puzzle!
Start from a certain letter and
continue to skip one letter at a
time to see if you can read
a sentence hidden around the
circle clockwise.

Circle letters (clockwise from top): O U T A D S I U F H E I M C W U H L A T T L I O H S T I O S F S P N X

'FLY FISHERS'

Unscramble the words to discover the fish Wullie and his pals have caught.

RUTTO DOC MONLAS
LAPICE SABSEAS

Ship ahoy!

Hidden in this wordsquare are ten different craft:

CANOE
YACHT
LINER
SCHOONER
DESTROYER
FRIGATE
TRAWLER
CRUISER
SUBMARINE
KAYAK

D	K	B	T	R	A	W	L	E	R
E	A	N	Y	O	P	R	I	E	V
S	Y	S	C	H	O	O	N	E	R
T	A	Z	I	L	T	I	E	N	E
R	K	A	Y	O	R	I	R	T	S
O	E	O	N	A	C	H	A	F	I
Y	A	R	M	I	C	L	E	D	U
E	N	B	O	L	T	H	I	A	R
R	U	F	R	I	G	A	T	E	C
S	O	R	V	A	T	E	N	G	O

The words are in a straight line, horizontally, vertically, or diagonally and may be read either forwards or backwards. Can you find them?

ANSWERS

JUST the JOB

Are you a Quick Quiz kid? Here's your chance to see how smart you are!

1. What is a male elephant called?
2. What, in olden days, was a "soutar"?
3. On which river does the city of Perth stand?
4. What is a nocturnal animal?
5. What is the maximum speed permitted on a motorway?
6. What game is played at Murrayfield?
7. What is the name of the one-legged pirate captain in "Treasure Island"?
8. "Tit for tat" is rhyming slang for what item of clothing?
9. What is the main dish at a Burns' Supper?
10. What does a farrier do?
11. Hurley is an Irish sport. What is its equivalent in Scotland?
12. What is greater — three feet or one metre?
13. What name is given to the small dirk worn in a kilted Scotman's hose?
14. Where in Edinburgh is the new Scottish parliament?
15. What famous statue stands in New York City's harbour?
16. Which Scottish actor plays Obi-Wan Kenobi in the recent Star Wars films?
17. In a traffic light sequence, what colour, or colours, follows green?
18. In which city would you find Covent Garden?
19. In showjumping, how many faults are awarded against a competitor who knocks down a fence?
20. How did the word "soap" come to describe TV and radio serials?
21. The Suez Canal runs through what country?

OOR WULLIE

See Maisie's cake fly through the air,
Then come doon wi' a clunk!
Nae wonder Wullie's pals decide
It's time tae dae a bunk!

ME AN' THE LADS ARE GOIN' TAE THE HIGHLAND GAMES TODAY!

OH, NO, WE'RE NOT! WE CANNA AFFORD IT!

INVERTUMSHIE HIGHLAND GAMES
TODAY
ADMISSION
ADULTS £3.00
WEANS £1.20
O.A.Ps FREE

COME ON! WE'LL HAE OOR AIN HIGHLAND GAMES!

WULLIE'S HOOSE

WE'LL START WI' THROWIN' THE HEAVY WEIGHT! THIS CAKE MAISIE SMITH BAKED ME WILL DAE FINE! IT'S BETTER THAN TRYIN' TAE EAT IT!

AYE, SHE'S THE WORST BAKER IN THE SCHOOL!

ME FIRST! HERE WE GO!

WULLIE! WHAT ARE YE DAEIN' WI' THAT CAKE I MADE YE?

MAISIE!

CRIVVENS! IT'S EVEN HEAVIER THAN I THOUGHT!

IT'S A LETHAL WEAPON!

IS THAT SO?

ER, THIS CAN BE PART O' OOR HIGHLAND GAMES, LADS! THE CROSS COUNTRY RACE!

IT'S SAFE, LADS! SHE'S GONE! LET'S HAVE THE TUG-O'-WAR NEXT!

I COULDNAE FIND A ROPE, BUT THIS SHEET WILL DAE!

DINNA WORRY! IT WAS AN AULD SHEET!

CRIVVENS!

RRIP!

Did you hear about the cat who ate a pound of cheese?

It waited for a mouse with baited breath!

Now, Danny, tell the class what you know about the Iron Age.

Er... I'm afraid I'm a bit rusty on that subject, sir.

LINE UP FOR LAUGHS!

By drawing five straight lines, divide the circle into eleven parts each of which contains only one bucket.

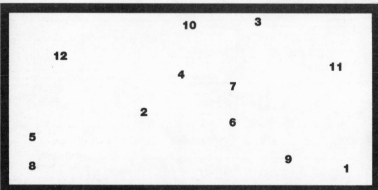

Draw four straight lines inside the frame so that each line passes through three different numbers.

SEE NEXT PAGE FOR ANSWERS

OOR WULLIE'S FUN SECTION

"I see the farmer's trying to grow mashed potatoes again!"

Lady Smith—"Goodness, Jane, where's the canary?"

New Maid—"I don't know, ma'am. It was there when I started cleaning its cage with the vacuum-cleaner!"

* * *

Jeannie—"You say your sister is a leading light in the cinema?"

Maggie—"Yes, she shows the people to their seats."

* * *

Tramp—"Will you give me ten pence for a sandwich?"

McGraw—"Let me see the sandwich first!"

* * *

"Training for a race?"
"No, racing for a train!"

McDonald—"I'm a mind reader, ye know!"

McLaren—"Really? Can you read my mind?"

McDonald—"No! I've left my magnifying glass at home!"

* * *

Diner—"Waiter, there are two flies fighting in my soup."

Waiter—"Well, what do you expect for ten pence—a bull-fight?"

* * *

"And the price is very reasonable—only ten thousand pounds."
"Ten thousand—and no stable?"
"Stable, sir?"
"Yes, for the ass who pays that much!"

Peem—"Have you ever laughed till you cried?"

Eck—"Yes. Only this morning Pa stepped on a tack and I laughed. Then Pa caught me laughing and I cried."

* * *

Tam—"You know that music stool you sold me?"

Tim—"Yes."

Tam—"Well, I've twisted and turned it in all directions, and I can't get a single tune out of it."

Ma—"Come along, Wullie, it's past time to get up."

Wullie—"Huh! It's no pastime for me—it's awfy hard work."

* * *

Customer—"Can I have my milk bill?"

Shopkeeper—"Excuse me, sir, my name isn't Bill, it's Tom."

* * *

Old Lady—"You say you were sent to prison for telling the truth?"

Convict—"Yes, lady. The judge asked me if I was guilty and I said ' yes '."

Answers to
LINE UP FOR LAUGHS

NUMBER PROBLEM –
Draw lines through
8,4,3 : 5,2,11 : 12, 6, 1 : 10, 7, 9.

ALL MUXED IP!

Belp m'hoab! Jivvens and crings! See if you can read this tunny fale written by WOOR ULLIE!

SANDY M^cTRAIL was a mandering winstrel who played the pagbipes. He was also the worst pagbipe player in the scand of Lots. Whenever he passed through a vittle lillage he used to plop and stay, and the people would glay padly to get rid of him.

It ho sappened that about this time a fierce rand of bobbers were plaguing the land. One night Sandy was harching through the mills when he nassed pear the hobber's ride-out. The robbers heard him coming in the darkness and way in lait to attack him. At this moment Sandy decided to play a tee wune to cheer himself up. So he struck up "The Pundred Hipers". When the bobbing rand heard the terrible row they ted in flerror.

The King of Scots heard about the frobbers' right and he sent for Sandy. "You shall be my bodyguard," he told him. "Whenever I am passing through a ponely lart of my land you shall pay your plipes and scare the bobbing rand away."

So Sandy, the worst player ever, became the first royal pagbipe player in all the land. And to this day nobody has been able to play the pag-bipes so badly!

OOR WULLIE

There's just nae peace for Boab today
When Wullie starts his jokin'.
But things don't go quite as Wull planned —
And guess who gets a soakin'!

Why did the chicken cross the road and come back again quickly?

Because his braces got caught in the lamp post!

You've saved my life. I must give you a reward.

Oh, no, I don't want any reward.

Oh, you must take something! Have you change of a pound?

Can you find at least fifteen items that begin with the letter "C"

PICTURE PROVERBS

Solve these picture puzzles to find
two well-known proverbs.

CE W ST B

H IX

Y SN M LD K

OOR WULLIE

Fat Boab's never far awa'
When there's a barbecue
He thinks he's affy smart, but och,
He can't beat you-know-who!

IT'S A BRAW DAY FOR A BARBECUE!

BUT I'LL HAE TAE THINK O' A WAY TAE KEEP FAT BOAB OOT!

HE CAN SNIFF OOT A SIZZLIN' SASSIDGE THREE MILES AWA'! ...

... IT JIST NEEDS HIM TAE MAK' UP ONE SANDWICH AND THERE'S NOTHING LEFT FOR ANYBODY ELSE!

... I DIDN'T ASK HIM LAST TIME ...

... I DIDNA REALISE HE WIS HIDIN' UNDER THE TABLE! ...

... THEN I TRIED PITTIN' A NOTICE OOTSIDE ...

DANGER BEWARE OF DOGS KEEP OOT

... BUT BOAB BROUGHT ALANG HIS FISHIN' LINE ...

BUT THIS TIME HE'S NO' GETTIN' NEAR THE GRUB!

I'M TURNING MY SHED INTAE FORT KNOX! ONCE IT'S A' PADLOCKED AND BARRED, BOAB WINNA GET A SNIFF O' THE GRUB!

AHEM! LOOK WHO'S HERE!

I'LL JIST GO AND GET THE GRUB NOW!

What is the difference between a nail and a bad boxer?

One gets knocked in and the other gets knocked out.

Did you want a plumber, lady?

Yes, I phoned you in January.

Wrong house, Harry.
The lady we're looking for
phoned last December!

CARTOON TIME

CRICKET CAPERS

HERE'S A GRAND CRICKET GAME TO GIVE YOU FUN

Two can play, or you can pick sides.
The batsman places a counter on the "Start" circle
and moves clockwise to the spin of
a coin – 4 circles forward for a "Head" and 1 for a "Tail".
How many runs can you score till you are out?

OOR WULLIE

All Wullie wants is some fresh air –
At least that's what he claims.
But he's glad when Ma puts an end
Tae a' his silly games!

WHERE IS HE TODAY?

PA'S MAKIN' ME STAY IN A' DAY BECAUSE I BROKE A WINDAE! ON A GRAND DAY LIKE THIS, TAE!

OCH, WELL, IF I'VE GOT TAE STAY IN, I MIGHT AS WELL OPEN THE DOOR AND GET SOME FRESH AIR!

WULLIE! WHAT HAVE YE DONE?

OPENED THE DOOR FOR SOME FRESH AIR!

YE MIGHT HAVE KNOWN MY BAKIN' WOULD ATTRACT THE FLIES!

I'LL OPEN THE FRONT DOOR INSTEAD! THAT'S WELL AWA' FRAE YER BAKING!

JINGS! THERE'S A STRONG DRAUGHT AT THIS END O' THE HOOSE!

WHOOSH!

YE DAFT GOWK! YE'VE RUINED MY BONNIE FLOOERS!

BUT I JUST WANTED SOME FRESH AIR!

I'LL OPEN THE SPARE ROOM WINDAE. THERE WON'T BE MUCH DRAUGHT AT THIS SIDE O' THE HOOSE!

OH, DEAR! JUST ENOUGH TAE BRING IN THE SMOKE FRAE MR McNAB'S BONFIRE NEXT DOOR!

Does it hurt when you stand on the scales?

No. Why?

Oh, because when Mum stands on them she always cries!

Now remember, Davie, there's a ghost in that cupboard where I keep the cake.

It's a funny thing, but you never blame the ghost when there's any cake missing.

FISHY BUSINESS

By starting from any four of the seven dots, Oor Wullie wants to catch four fish that will bring him at least sixteen kilogrammes. Trace along the lines and add the weights of the four fish you can catch to see if you can beat him.

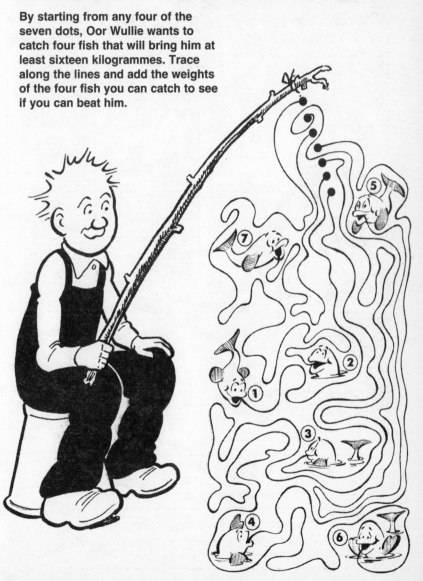

GREAT SPORT!

EACH OF THE WORDS IN COLUMN 'A' CAN BE LINKED TO ONE OF THE SPORTS IN COLUMN 'B'. CAN YOU PAIR THEM OFF?

A	B
SWEEP	GOLF
RUCK	RUGBY
GATE	TENNIS
SLIPS	SNOOKER
DOUBLE	SAILING
BULLY-OFF	SHOW-JUMPING
EAGLE	HOCKEY
SIDE	CRICKET
SHEET	BOWLS
DEUCE	DARTS
JACK	SKIING
FAULT	CURLING

ANSWERS *

SWEEP–CURLING : RUCK–RUGBY : GATE–SKIING : SLIPS–CRICKET : DOUBLE–DARTS : BULLY-OFF–HOCKEY : EAGLE–GOLF : SIDE–SNOOKER : SHEET–SAILING : DEUCE–TENNIS : JACK–BOWLS : FAULT–SHOW-JUMPING.

SPOT THE DIFFERENCES

There are eight small differences between these two pictures. See if you can find them all.

OOR WULLIE

See Oor Wullie's summer ploy's —
He tries some "deep-sea" fishin',
And then he leads his three pals on
A jungle-trekkin' mission!

JINGS! THESE SUMMER HOLIDAYS HAVE BEEN GREAT!

THE THINGS I'VE DONE SINCE THE SCHOOL CAME AFF . . .

. . . I INVENTED A NEW GEMME . . .

GOAL!

HUH! I DINNA THINK THIS FITBA'-CRICKET WILL CATCH ON, WULLIE!

. . . I WON A DAFT BET . . .

AN' I SAY IT'S IMPOSSIBLE TO GO SLEDGIN' IN SUMMER!

JUST YOU WATCH!

HELTER SKELTER

NEXT TIME, USE A MAT, LIKE A'BODY ELSE!

THERE YE ARE! YOU OWE ME FOWER BEANOS!

. . . I MADE THE WORLD'S BIGGEST SANDCASTLE WITHOOT GOIN' TAE THE BEACH . . .

IT'S A' VERY WELL YOU BUILDIN' A CASTLE, WULLIE . . .

. . . BUT WE'RE WAITIN' TAE BUILD A HOOSE!

. . . AND I WENT DEEP-SEA FISHIN' . . .

HEY, TONY —

I DINNA SUPPOSE YE'VE ANY REJECT, IMPERFECT FISH SUPPERS, JUST IN CASE I HAPPEN TAE MEET A STARVIN' CAT?

DEEP-SEA FISH RESTAURANT

AWA' WI' YE NOW, WULLIE! THAT'S THE LAST FREE SUPPER YE GET THIS SUMMER!

A weary-looking man who had been
looking for a job for months happened to see a
police poster headed "Thief Wanted".
"Well," he said, "it's better than nothing, anyway.
I'm going to ask for the job!"

Why does that big cannibal look at us so strangely?

Perhaps he's the food inspector!

Word Ladder

If you fill in the clues correctly, the words in the boxes reading down will give you the name of Wullie's favourite mouse. (We've put in some letters to help you.)

1.
2. **T**
3. **L**
4.
5. **E**

1. You spread this on bread.
2. A fierce stripey animal.
3. Party food eaten with ice cream.
4. Football is one.
5. What we see with.

OOR WULLIE

An ambush set for Wullie by
Three laddies, sair offended!
He fools them a', but then he finds
The danger hasnae ended!

I'M NO' GOIN' OOT TODAY. I SOAKED THE LADS WI' MY WATER PISTOL YESTERDAY, AND THEY'LL BE OOT FOR REVENGE!

WULLIE! TAK' THIS PARCEL ROOND TAE AULD TAM SMITH!

B-BUT ....

NAE 'BUTS', AFF YE GO!

AND SO ....

THIS'LL KEEP MY HEID DRY ANYWAY!

WAA! MY GOLDFISH BAG IS LEAKIN'!

WULLIE'S HOOSE

QUICK, WULLIE. GIES A LEN' O' YOUR HELMET!

THANKS, WULLIE!

HMPH!

I'LL WEAR PA'S NEW RAINCOAT. THAT'LL KEEP ME DRY!

BUT ....

YIKES!

TRIP

OOYAH!

CRUNCH!

I'LL BORROW MA'S UMBERELLY!

WULLIE'S HOOSE

Where do cows dance?

A disc-cow-theque!

What's the difference between a lion with a toothache and a rainy day?

One roars with pain and the other pours with rain!

SPOT THE DIFFERENCES!

There are eight small differences between these two pictures. See if you can find them all.

While you're at it, can you draw Wullie's Sheriff's Star without taking your pencil off the paper or crossing a line? Turn over the page if you're stuck!

CLOOTIE DUMPLING!

See how many words you can make, using the letters in CLOOTIE DUMPLING. Plurals and proper names are not allowed. Put your words in the space below.

How to draw the Sheriff's Star.

Did you hear about the lady who was knocked down by horses?

She's reported to be in a stable condition!